Dark and Bloodied Ground

Dark and

Bloodied Ground

Photographs by Mary Eastman

Text by Mary Bolté

The Chatham Press, Inc.
Riverside, Connecticut

Library of Congress Catalog Card No.: 73-83357

SBN 85699-802-5

Photographic print processing by Terry Hourigan

Printed in the United States of America
by The Murray Printing Company

CONTENTS

PREFACE

Few regions of our country are marked by such topographical disparity as the Border States. Continuity and consistency suffer in the land. The traveler can behold the great broad uncertain rivers which bore pioneers to the west, a wild and treacherous ocean coast, and cloven in between, the dark tumbled peaks and ridges of the Cumberland. It is, all of it, bloodied ground indeed. The conquest of its wilderness by a violent and often outcast people cost a torrent of blood, while bitter feuds spilled more under a code of law which, more often than not, left retribution to the arbitrary passions of the individual.

And parts of it were bloodied almost beyond belief by the War between the States.

Tales of evil flourished here. They still do. The bargaining Devil rides the windy beaches, and some awful presence skirts and lurks, with equal malignancy, through the murky lowland swamps and the lonely shadowed mountain creeks. Ghosts plague both the elegant mansion and the lonely cabin with the same persistence. In much of the beautiful isolated terrain, time has stood still for descendants of the frontier folk. Pocketed, preserved, ringed round by hallelujah hills, a proud and independent people naturally nourish their folklore. Soap-making, planting and hog butchering are performed by the phases of the moon. Cures and curses centuries old are still administered with ancient potions. The primeval art of voodoo came long ago up-river from New Orleans and remains lodged in the hills.

Nothing rests easy here.

In tenacious legend, this misty river, sea and mountain place cherishes its tempers, its ghosts, a clever Beelzebub, menacing witches, the hollow countenance of the slain, and above all an ominous ever-present sense of the supernatural.

Legends have a habit of existing in many forms; details vary from

telling to telling. For this reason there seems to be no such thing as an authentic version, to which the present collection has no claim. Storytelling of this sort is not so much an exercise in accurate history as it is in entertainment. The same principle applies to the photographs. While most have been made at or near the reputed scene of the legend, a few liberties have been taken to help express a particular mood. But just as ghosts tend to vanish in the light of day, so do ghostly tales fade before any insistence on authenticity.

—MARY BOLTÉ
Dresden, Maine
April, 1973

Outlaws and Killers

SAM MASON, RIVER PIRATE

Henderson, Kentucky

If ever a territory was tailor-made for brigands it would be the broad river country of the Mid-South. An abundance of hide-outs and escape routes attracted thieves who specialized in barges and keelboats bearing valuable cargoes of goods and money. Among the many notorious out-laws of this persuasion, Samuel Mason earned high marks for shrewd-ness and cruelty.

A Virginian by birth, a gentleman and a soldier of distinction, Mason belonged to that category of unfortunates who are thrust, by only a quirk of fate, out of a law-abiding life and into a career of crime. Mason's transformation began in the 1790's when his daughter fell in love with an unsavory fellow involved with a gang of cutthroats who preyed on emigrants voyaging down the Ohio River. When the two young people ran off together, Mason's immediate reaction was to disown his daugh-ter. Later he apparently relented, and planned an elaborate party in her honor at his homestead in Henderson, Kentucky, just south of Evansville, Indiana. He even invited his daughter's lover. The reception (or "infare" as it was called in pioneer society) was such a splendid one, copious of food and drink, that it wasn't until the gala was well along that someone noticed the groom was missing. Search parties were dispatched, though they did not have far to go. A bloody, crumpled body was found beneath the tulip tree, the vengeful work of Mason's three sons. In the space of an evening the handsome, upright gentleman from Virginia was embroiled in the very life of violence he so deplored in his daughter's lover. Nor was there any turning back; fleeing from his home and his wife, Mason, along with his sons, had to shoot and kill the pursuing sheriff. The fugitives then headed for Cave-in-Rock. This remarkable limestone formation on the Illinois side of the Ohio River, one hundred miles upstream from Cairo, had long been a refuge

for Indians as well as French and Colonial traders; but it was Mason (now alias Wilson) who turned it into a headquarters for organized banditry. Mason called his den "The Liquor Vault and House of Entertainment," an inviting title which he printed on a crude sign on the river bank to lure unwary flatboat captains and their passengers into his grasp. Often the victims were murdered, their bodies weighted with pebbles to insure sinkage, and dropped into the river. After depriving a boat of its cargo Mason sometimes sent the vessel on down-river to be sold at New Orleans. Cave-in-Rock came to be dreaded by traders far more than the perilous falls of the Ohio up-river or the treacherous Hurricane Island passage below.

When Mason eventually moved south, his murderous sphere of operation increased to encompass territory stretching all the way to the city of Natchez, Mississippi. So greatly was he feared that from the Mississippi banks to the Tennessee highlands, any sight of a buzzard soaring overhead would occasion the remark: "Another murder by the Mason gang."

Like many another desperado, Mason met his end through treachery. In 1803 when Governor Claibourne of the Mississippi Territory placed a large reward on the head of the bandit, two of Mason's men determined to collect it. While engaged with their leader in counting some ill-gotten loot, one of them reached for a hatchet. A short time later the henchmen arrived in Natchez carrying a sturdy sack. Inside the poke was a large ball of hardened clay which, when broken, proved the bearers to be just claimants to the reward. The ironic postscript to the tale is that the traitors were soon recognized as Mason's men (one had also previously been a member of the notorious Harpe gang) and were subsequently tried and hanged.

JOHN BROWN'S TAVERN

Chattanooga, Tennessee

Back in 1803 before the Cherokee were forced to vacate all the land
east of the Mississippi, a two-story log house was erected under the
shadow of Lookout Mountain at Moccasin Bend in the Tennessee River.
It was run as a tavern by a resourceful member of the tribe, John Brown.

The site was located along an increasingly important trading route
and it was later to become the city of Chattanooga. Brown's tavern
became a popular stopping place for traders bearing gold jewelry and
watches, imported shawls, highgrade tools, Pennsylvania rifles and kid
gloves.

At the south end of William Island, the Indian also ran a ferry
which linked up with the stage route around Lookout Mountain, the
only negotiable passageway between the markets of the South and the
eastern territory. Brown's position was indeed a comfortable one. His
amiable disposition must have pleased his ferry customers and insured
the popularity of his tavern, for according to legend, he was a born
storyteller.

Brown could be counted on to fascinate and entertain his clientele
with endless Cherokee tales of underground panthers, slant-eyed giants
and haunted whirlpools. He was generous, too, in his distribution of

elegant handcrafted tobacco pipes and the hostel's bill of fare. That the Cherokee prospered was not surprising, and if he sometimes sported ornaments and clothing of uncommon, even exotic quality, it was easily assumed that his own generosity was frequently repaid.

Sometimes Brown's guests did not stay through the entire night, but departed long before sunrise to "make an early start to it," the Indian explained. No suspicion was aroused until a tavern guest with a particularly valuable cargo subsequently failed to arrive at his destination in Franklin, North Carolina; but even that was shrugged off when Brown suggested to those who questioned the matter that any wagon as decrepit as the one belonging to the Franklin trader was surely unlikely to survive the rough mountain trip.

A cry in the night, the splintering of wood from the blow of an

ax, a sudden splash in the water—these noises failed to bother the traders. They kept right on arriving at Brown's tavern and, every once in a while, leaving in the dead of night. And John Brown kept right on running his ferry, feeding his guests and getting richer. When, in 1838, the Cherokees were expelled from the area, Brown was included, though he was surely one of the wealthiest of the unwilling emigrants. But he was free—as free as any Indian could be. He had not been convicted of a single crime. He had not even been accused.

It wasn't until over a half a century later that dredging operations in the Tennessee River uncovered grim testimony to the Indian's avocation. Strewn like stepping stones along the riverbed, directly in line with John Brown's ferry route, were dozens of rotted wagon wheels and half again as many bones.

A PEDDLER KILLER

Bigbend, Calhoun County, West Virginia

With his supply of ready cash the vagabond peddler was too often an easy mark for greedy, unscrupulous citizens. Murdered peddlers were common figures in American folklore. Frequently their killers went scot-free, especially in the narrow valleyed terrain of the Border States where law was often weakly enforced. From Calhoun County in West Virginia comes a tale of one such murderer who was, however, exposed.

John Mason was a stranger to the region. Even after he bought a tract of land in the hamlet of Bigbend, southeast of Parkersburg, and built a small cabin, his background remained mysterious. But being a churchgoer and an amiable fellow he was soon accepted by the community. Men began to drop by his cabin to swap stories and include him in their evening 'coon hunts. On such an outing one of the party slipped on a beech log and fell into a chilly creek. Immediately Mason invited the hunter and his friends to stop at his cabin and dry out before the fire.

As Mason passed around tin cups of corn whiskey the conversation turned to one of the riddles of the valley—the disappearance of Sam Conners, a likable old peddler who made his rounds carrying wares in a black oilcloth poke.

"Did you know Conners, John?" asked Jim Davis, one of the hunters. "I thought you might because of these cups. Old Sam sold me some just like them."

Mason replied that he'd never met the peddler and had bought the cups at a store over in the next county.

Almost immediately after he'd spoken, the hunters' hounds outside set up a long, mournful wailing and soon after that the floorboards of the cabin creaked strangely and the door swung slowly open.

"Who's out there?" called Davis.

"Must have been the wind," Mason put in mildly.

Davis rose and went to close the door. There was no wind.

Again the floorboards creaked. The men looked uneasily at each other.

"The freezing ground must be pushing up the floor," Mason said. "Guess I didn't dig the footings deep enough."

The visitors stood up, shuffled their feet and, picking up their rifles, nervously bade their host good night. Once outside they could feel the nip of the night air, though all were aware that the ground was not freezing.

"Maybe," said Davis, "we should help you shore up the footings of the cabin." Mason rather forcefully declined their offer but the more he protested the more insistent became his friends. They would not take no for an answer.

When the group gathered at the cabin the next morning with their tools, John Mason met them carrying a leather pouch. With a smile, he announced that he had to go into town on urgent business but was mighty pleased to have the help of his friends.

The men set to work. Since the ground was not frozen, the digging

wasn't difficult, and before long Jim Davis' shovel hit something that clinked. He reached down and withdrew a small tin saucer. Silently the men gathered around to examine the article. When they returned to their chore, more saucers were uncovered, then an oilcloth pack, and finally the skeleton of the poor peddler himself, his bony arms upraised as if to fend off the earth under which Mason had buried him alive.

John Mason was apprehended by sheer chance at Creston, five miles up the Little Kanawaha River on his way to Parkersburg. After refreshing himself at a tavern he had taken out a brown and red leather money pouch to pay for his whiskey. Another patron at the bar put a hand on his arm.

"Mind if I look at your bag? Only seen one like it ever before."

Mason gave a start and quickly seized the bag, pulling it toward him. As he did so it split in two, scattering the coins. But what interested the other man were the initials "S.C." on the lining.

"Thought it looked like Sam's," said the sheriff of Creston. "Better come along with me."

BLUEBEARD HARRY POWERS

Quiet Dell, West Virginia

To conceal the clothing of a murdered mistress in a bureau drawer beneath the wedding gown of one's wife requires a fanciful mind. Such imagination and more had Harry F. Powers, swain to over a hundred corresponding ladies under the name of Cornelius O. Pierson. Known as the Mail-order Lover, he shocked the nation in 1931 when his property in Quiet Dell, West Virginia, yielded up five gory corpses. Overnight the tiny hamlet three miles from Clarksburg was thronged with sight-seers, as well as a number of imaginative entrepreneurs seeking to charge admission to tour his farm.

The story of Harry Powers unfolds like an evil flower, each opening petal revealing a further chamber of calculated brutality until the final stamen of horror appears.

His wooing career began with his marriage to Luella Strother, whose tragic history included her previous marriage to one Ernest Knisley, himself convicted of murdering a neighbor named John Wheeler in 1902. What Luella's fate was eventually intended to be at the hands of her second husband remains a mystery, as does the number of victims he might have had in other parts of the country.

The ardent letter-writer apparently modeled his epistles after those of Rudolph Valentino, and spuriously presented himself as handsome, well-to-do and of uncommonly high morals. It is not surprising that he had none of these attributes but rather pursued his fiendish crimes in the grips of a desperate greed for money. The women he wooed through the American Friendship Society were wealthy, often widowed and always lonely. Powers' method was to promise them lasting affection, a good life and freedom from the burden of handling their fortunes, which were consigned to him for safekeeping.

One of Powers' correspondents was a woman from Park Ridge,

Illinois, a widow with three children named Mrs. Asta Eicher. After several weeks of letter-writing, Powers apparently induced her to become his wife. He drove to Illinois to take her back to Clarksburg and then returned to fetch her children, with promises of ponies and trips to Europe. Park Ridge neighbors became uneasy when he whisked the children away so hurriedly that one was still wearing his bathing suit. Deeper suspicion arose sometime later when a former boarder and suitor of Mrs. Eicher's came across Powers piling up the widow's furniture in her garage, and offering the puzzling explanation that he had purchased the house and was planning to live there. The following day he was gone. The inevitable questions could not fail to eventually lead the law to Powers' farm in Quiet Dell. What was found there was a nightmare. In the garage were several cells in which the murderer starved his victims. A rope hung from a joist over a trapdoor leading to a bloodstained vault below. It was into this chamber that the bodies of Mrs. Eicher and her children had been dropped, some strangled, others hammered to death, to be buried afterwards in the sewage ditch outside. Nor were the Eichers the only victims. A fifth body, that of the Widow Lemke from Northboro, Massachusetts, was also unearthed and, according to Powers' correspondence, more were scheduled to join them.

Powers' wife, by this time a virtual recluse who thus far had said nothing against her husband, now denounced the mass murderer as did citizens all across the nation, many of whom were certain that vanished loved ones had fallen victim to this same monstrous fiend.

When the time came for Harry's trial, the Clarksburg Courthouse was undergoing repairs. Thus the courtroom scene took place instead on the stage of a movie house, where Powers, doomed to hang as one of America's most atrocious criminals, drew a greater audience that September than the subsequent Lunt-Fontanne cinematic performance of The Guardsman.

Witches and Hants

THE BELL WITCH

Adams, Tennessee

"Pretty as sin" was the way some people described Kate Batts, "and kindly as the Devil."

Whether Kate fitted the description is a matter for speculation, but she surely did bedevil the Bell family. Early in the nineteenth century, soon after righteous John Bell had purchased a tract of Mrs. Batts' land to supplement his own extensive property near Springfield, Kate accused the pious man of cheating her. This conviction she held for the rest of her life, and on her deathbed she took an oath to "hant John Bell and all his kith and kin as long as he is above ground."

Spectral Kate's favorite victims were John and his daughter Betsy. Often during the day furniture fell and dishes flew, noses were tweaked and hair was pulled. And through the night they claimed to feel the weight of her spirit riding mercilessly upon their backs. But worst of all were the ghostly threats. No one in the Bell family could predict when Kate's haunting voice might split the wind with dark warnings of imminent death or disaster. To Mrs. Bell, whom she apparently held in affection, her admonitions were often solicitous: "Stay indoors tomorrow, ma'am. There'll be a bad storm, for I saw the cats and rats aplaying after sundown."

The awful spirit's favorite verse which she sang often and hollowly to John Bell was this:

> *Hairy John Bell,*
> *the banks know you well*
> *and they take good care of your money.*
> *Put your gold in a sack*
> *'cause you ain't coming back.*
> *The Devil will tend to your gunny.*

The fearful apparition did not confine herself only to the Bell household. According to participants, she made frequent wavering appearances at revival meetings where her dreadful moaning outdid the most ardent converts. She apparently loved corn whiskey, too, and was said to be an habitual raider of stills. When hopping drunk she would be sure to whistle back to the Bell house to torment John and Betsy afresh. When Betsy fell in love with a young farmer named Josiah Gardner, Kate hexed the romance to such an extent that the terrified and beleaguered Gardner capitulated and fled the state.

No charms against the witch's wrath—salt sprinkled on the hearth, a Bible under the pillow, the left hind foot of a graveyard rabbit buried in the pocket—were of any effect. Old Kate's ghost persisted. Her fame spread, and the Bell farm became as feared a spot as the cemetery at midnight.

Finally gossip about Kate reached the ears of Andrew Jackson down in Nashville. One evening in 1815, after a certain amount of whiskey, Old Hickory set forth with a company of friends, determined to confront the spook and banish it forever. Kate's shade was on guard. At the edge of the Bell property Jackson's mules adamantly halted—as only mules can. Nobody in the party could budge the animals or the wagon. Suddenly, above Jackson's string of curses, was heard on the wind Kate's whining howl. "All right, General. You can move on. I'll see you later this evening." She kept her word. All night long the ghost of Kate Batts molested the Bell house, particularly the General's suite. She sang, she swore, tables were upset and glassware smashed, and in the early morning hours the Bells' harpsichord produced dirges played by unseen hands. A weary and defeated Jackson left the house in the morning, declaring, "I'd rather fight the British again than have dealings with that witch."

Presumably the intimidation of Andrew Jackson was the ghost's finest hour. John Bell, now hopelessly beseiged, pitifully declined to his grave, whereupon the spirit of Kate Batts vanished and was heard from no more. Or perhaps not. Local people say that when Kate died, her body was thrown down a well behind the Bell house and that every two years her spirit rises to haunt a nearby cave in which ghostly echoes of her threats can still be heard.

OLD MANSION

Bowling Green, Virginia

Embraced by graceful terraced gardens and gnarled spreading boxwood, Old Mansion was once not only a grand Bowling Green estate, but also the setting for tragedy.

Built by Major John Hoomes on land patented to him in 1670, the big wood and brick house with its steep-hipped gambrel roof was eventually inherited by his great grandson, Colonel John Waller Hoomes, a sportsman and proud father of three sons. The Colonel imported horses, and although most of the thoroughbreds came from Britain, a few were shipped from Spain. A Spanish dealer, convinced that Hoomes had cheated him out of the price of a valuable Barb stallion, sailed to America to claim his money. Hoomes greeted the elegantly clad merchant most civilly and took him in, after which the Spaniard was never seen again.

Some time later, the sociable Hoomes gave a dinner at the mansion to celebrate the arrival of another highly prized Spanish pony. Invited were only the most elite of the county gentry, as well as Hoomes' three sons. The long table was set for thirteen. When, between sherbet and viand, the Colonel formally raised his glass in toast to his new acquisition, two other things happened. An explosive sound was heard as if horses were galloping around the circular drive outside the house. And Hoomes' eldest son fainted. Servants and guests alike rushed to attend the boy, while others hurried to the windows to glimpse the horses. But though the sound of galloping continued no horses were visible in the dark.

The following morning the boy died. Clutched in the lad's hand, his father found a Spanish doubloon.

Several months later, the Colonel, somewhat recovered from grief, had resumed enough of his mantle of conviviality to give another party,

this time enlarging the gathering to thirty guests. Among the assembly was pretty Amanda Soule. Although only thirteen years old, Amanda showed vivid promise of becoming one of Virginia's most dazzling and sought-after belles. No one was more aware of this than Hoomes' second son, Henry. At the time his father was preparing a toast to celebrate a recent victory at the track, Henry was listening with fervid attention to the charming girl's flirtatious prattle. At precisely the moment the host lifted his glass of muscatel, a thunder of hoofs seemed to split the great room and the Colonel's second son fell lifeless to the floor, as a gold coin rolled from his hand across the parqueted floor.

As before, no horses were seen in the gloom.

Three years of mourning ensued. It was Colonel Hoomes' reckless nature that finally led him to gamble once more, this time with the life of his remaining heir, William. On the young man's twenty-first birthday his father gave an enormous gala, not only to celebrate the date of the lad's birth, but also his engagement to Amanda Soule, now more exquisite than ever. The finest of wines were uncorked to accompany the choicest of hams and wild fowl. A full chamber orchestra provided music for waltzes under the glittering chandeliers and at midnight a flotilla of footmen appeared bearing silver trays laden with champagne.

"And now," cried the smiling Colonel, lifting his crystal goblet, "for my gift to William and his betrothed." Reaching behind him, he pulled a gold tasseled cord; green velvet portieres parted to reveal two magnificent chestnut yearlings. The guests gasped at their beauty and they gasped when, at exactly that moment, the thunder of ghostly hoofbeats was heard once again. William, putting a hand to his heart, fell lifeless to the floor, his pale cheek thudding softly against a gold doubloon.

People say that thrice a year, on the anniversaries of each boy's death, the phantom hoofs can be heard on the darkened grounds galloping round and round and round the lovely, tragic house.

BROWN MOUNTAIN LIGHTS

Morganton, North Carolina

Happily this North Carolina phenomenon still remains one of the unsolved mysteries of our planet. These erratic lights, which pop up thick
and fast like glowing champagne corks over the mountain rim, have
intrigued residents, visitors and even scientists for years. In 1771 a
German, Gerard William de Brahn, explained the sometimes bluish,
sometimes reddish illuminations as nitrous vapors and sulphates mixed
together by crossing winds. In 1913, the United States Geological Survey
concluded that the lights were locomotive headlights shining up from
tracks along the Catawba Valley. (The theory lost credibility after a
disastrous flood wiped out the railroad bridges in 1916 without affecting
the appearance of the Brown Mountain lights.)

In 1919 the Weather Bureau reported a similarity between the North
Carolina lights and a curious phenomenon in the Andes of South America.
Next the Geological surveyors resumed research only to dismiss the
cause as the spontaneous combustion of marsh gases. But there weren't
any marshes in the vicinity. They also discarded the notion that the
lights were a reflection of fires under moonshine stills. The report read:
"There are not enough such stills and probably would not be in suf-
ficiently continous operation to produce lights in the number and regu-
larity of those seen at Brown Mountain."

Such fruitless investigations ease the way toward believing the
Cherokee legend, for Indians knew of the lights centuries ago. Once
the Cherokee and Catawba Indians engaged in a great battle below
Brown Mountain. Today, as one climbs the mountain, the lights diminish
and finally vanish altogether. The legend claims that these disappearing
lights are the fleeing ghosts of torch-bearing Indian maidens who endlessly search through the flame-colored azaleas on the hillside for
their sweethearts wounded in battle.

FRANCIE

Francie was born in 1929. Since then she's become familiar in the region. A great many motorists will tell you so.

She wears a mauve-colored dress, the one in which she died. When you see her outstretched thumb and stop your car or truck to pick her up, perhaps on Route 119, you'll notice that her clothes are wringing wet and no matter how high you turn up the heater, or how many coats and blankets you pile upon her, she never stops her shivering. She smiles gaily while she talks but her chattering teeth give her speech a stutter. When you let her out on the outskirts of Molus and she says "Th-th-thank you. M-mother will b-b-be w-waiting," you wonder if the poor soaked girl will ever make it to the dimly lit cabin on the hill. You wonder and wonder, and if you don't stop to scramble up the muddy path to the hilltop cabin on your next trip down from Cumberland, chances are you will when you travel up from Middlesboro. A worn old woman in faded pink will open the door, and when you ask if her daughter arrived home safely she'll shake her head and say wearily, "Another visitor, are you? A careless driver run Francie into the creek back in '49." Then the old woman will gaze up wistfully and ask, "You wouldn't of knowed who it was, would you, that killed poor Francie?"

THE LOVERS OF
DISMAL SWAMP

near Poughkeepsie, Virginia

The eerie terrain of the aptly named Dismal Swamp, spanning the eastern Virginia-North Carolina border, readily lends itself to ghostly tales. Queer lights sometimes emanate from the oozing bogs, flickering along the bony cypress knees. Lush cinnamon ferns and creepers crowd the spongy hummocks. Snakes and slippery creatures lurk furtively in the slime. All about there is the sweet perfume of decay.

One of the common legends of the place concerns a long-ago young Sioux brave whose beloved fell ill and died. When her body was interred near the Great Swamp, the inconsolable Indian spent many days at the site brooding over his loss. Finally in the depths of his grief, reason left him and he became convinced that the girl was not dead but had been taken away by evil spirits and was being held somewhere in the vastness of the swamp in desperate need of rescue. For weeks he wandered the periphery of the bog, among dogwood and possumhaw, waiting for a sign to reveal the whereabouts of her captivity. One twilight a swarm of tiny, flickering lights appeared beckoning to him from across the murky water. Convinced that the fiery cluster was the signal he had awaited, the Indian put together a frail craft of white cedar bark and sweet gum leaves and set forth to rescue his sweetheart. Days later his ruined vessel was found but nowhere was there any trace of his body. The young brave did find his love, it is said, for on soft summer nights a pale canoe bearing two dim figures can be seen gliding in silence across the still, steaming swamp, obscured in mist but surely guided at the bow by a band of flickering fireflies.

CONJURATION AGAINST FEONA

Pine Creek, West Virginia

Feona Willis had designs on Petey Bay and everybody knew it. But Petey loved Ruthann, and everybody knew that, too.

Feona was the daughter of recently deceased Old Mol Willis who had been commonly considered a witch. Hadn't the Mosely baby come down with thrash and the Bakers' sheep died after visits from Mol? And when Abel Gorse was found dead of a poisonous mushroom hadn't there been a black cat with eyes as green as Mol's slinking 'round the spicebush? Most Pine Creek folk suspected that Mol had passed her occult powers on to Feona and they didn't hold out much hope for Petey and Ruthann's marriage. Bound to be trouble.

They were right.

Trouble started on the wedding night. In the morning Petey claimed that someone had been riding him all night long, as though he were a horse, and lashing him with briar whips. In the light of day Ruthann could plainly see the scarlet marks upon his back. They both knew Feona was behind it all. And when at sunset Petey started dancing quick and jerky steps all by himself, they knew that was Feona's work, too.

Ruthann tried every remedy she knew. She laid a broom and a Bible across the doorstep, for a witch must count every straw and every page before she can enter a house—and such a task could take all night. She drew a picture of Feona on the gatepost and spat upon it every hour.

Nothing worked. Every twilight poor, bewitched Petey skittered and pranced like a bee-stung hound, and every morning he awoke exhausted and sore. One day Ruthann heard about two black ladies living in nearby Williamson, just across the Tug Fork branch of the Big Sandy River. Long ago these women had come up from Trinidad via Alabama, and were reputedly able to remove a witch's curse. When they agreed to

help Ruthann, they told her they first must have a ball of wax, a hunk of Feona's hair and some "goober dust" from Mol Willis' burial mound.

The ball of wax was no trouble, but the other two tasks were not to Ruthann's liking. "Goober dust" was grave soil. Ruthann didn't especially enjoy graves and certainly not Mol Willis'. As for Feona, she hardly dared go near her, much less ask her for a hank of hair.

But Ruthann was a plucky girl who meant to keep her man. One windy afternoon she got her grit up and, carrying a knotted kerchief, started up the knob toward the graveyard. Midway she spied Feona, her long dark hair blowing out behind her. Quickly Ruthann hid behind an elderberry bush until Feona had passed, then she scrambled up the hill and, squeezing her eyes tight shut, grabbed a scattermint of dirt from Mol Willis' grave and scrunched it into her kerchief. The wind was blowing harder now. Down in the narrow valley the aspen leaves, all turned inside out, were dancing like the disks in a gypsy's tambourine.

Just as Ruthann reached the last decline of the knob, three long strands of black hair, hooked over an alder branch, blew across her path. Swiftly Ruthann untangled them and popped them into her kerchief.

The next day she took the wax, the "goober dust" and Feona's hair to the conjurers.

"Spread mustard seed and jimson weed beneath your step and come again in two days' time, with a white candle," they told her.

Ruthann obeyed, and returned to the dark cabin forty-eight hours later. In the gloom she could barely make out the figures, but she heard one say, "Sit here, close by the candle." The candle was lighted and as it burned down, a tiny doll-like image of Feona appeared, which seemingly melted away as the wick was consumed. In the dark the two old women smiled at Ruthann.

The next morning the charred body of Feona Willis was found beside the hearth of her cabin, which had burned to the ground.

The Mountain People

A SOLDIER AND HIS DOG

Peter's Creek Valley, West Virginia

Among the mountain folk of Scotch-Irish-English descent the spectral dog commands a prominent position in legend. Unlike the terrorizing hound in the west of England "cantering dark and ragged as a cloud across a moor moon," the Appalachian ghost dog is saffron-colored, often spotted and not really threatening.

Mountaineers cherished and depended upon their dogs, and if a canine apparition appeared to a man riding back from collecting salt at Morgantown, he wasn't really surprised. On the lonesome twilight road the loping phantom dog was company, and when it rose and glided along in the air, skimming the horse's head, the traveler was often glad that three made a crowd.

Slain dogs were another matter.

In the deep-ravined area near Summersville, where sunlight seldom penetrates the stands of hickory and ash, it is rumored that the wraiths of a soldier and his whimpering dog traverse the narrow huckle-berry-bordered byway in the hours just before daylight. During the War between the States, a group of tired and frightened young recruits became lost here behind enemy lines. After they had decided to camp for the night in the precipitous valley, they were alarmed to see the company cook seized with a series of violent tremors and a high scorch-ing fever. Neither horehound tea, nor a dose of cherrybark bitters, nor even a freshly split toad bound to the sick man's throat seemed to be of any help. At last delirium and then unconsciousness overcame the cook, convincing the soldiers that his death from some terrible plague was inevitable. Terrified of infection, his comrades buried him as quickly as they could—alive.

Sang, the cook's dog, bayed so mournfully beside his master's grave that eventually the soldiers feared he would arouse the enemy. To silence him, the panic-stricken men crushed the animal's skull and buried him near his friend.

The exhausted troop then collapsed beneath the witch hazel bushes

to sleep. Scarcely a quarter of an hour had passed before they were awakened by the sound of scratching and a doleful whine. Wearily rubbing their eyes, the men looked up to see Sang's freshly opened grave and the dog himself, vaporous as sulphur in the first gauzy gray of dawn, pawing away at the burial mound of his master.

No one in Peter's Creek Valley accepts bets on how long it took

the troops to break camp, but old-timers claim that Sang dug up his master all right, because the company cook has since been seen just before the moon fades, wavering feverishly down the deep-shadowed valley searching for help and followed by his faithful pet. And, they say, if the wind is right, you can hear Sang's melancholy wail threading through the dale and echoing back, over and over and over again.

THE HATFIELDS AND McCOYS

Omar, West Virginia

Of all the feuds which took place in the steep ragged ridges along the West Virginia-Kentucky line, none was more bitter or notorious than the Hatfield-McCoy fracas which ricocheted through forest, hill and creek for nearly fifteen years.

Stories about the beginnings of the feud differ. Most people believe it started in 1882 when young Jonse Hatfield of Logan County, West Virginia, ran off with Rosanna McCoy of Pike County, Kentucky. The abduction angered the McCoy clan, and during the flare-up that followed Ellison Hatfield was shot. Three McCoy brothers were arrested, and as they were taken to the Pikeville jail a posse of Hatfields led by Devil Anse, clan chieftain, abducted the three men, carrying them to the West Virginia side of the Tug Fork of the Big Sandy River. When Ellison died, the Hatfields rowed the McCoy boys back to Kentucky and shot them dead on their own soil. And thus began a war of hatred and revenge between the two families that became a way of life. From then on Hatfields and McCoys shot each other on sight. Even a trivial disagreement over the number of notches on a hog's ear (a form of branding used by mountaineers) would set the clans off on a shooting spree.

Arrests were useless. When Hatfields were apprehended in Logan County, where practically every other deputy was a relative, they were without fail acquitted. The same was true for the McCoy clan whose relations held offices in Pike County. Even the governors of the two states engaged in heated arguments, Governor Wilson of West Virginia refusing to honor Governor Buckner's plea to extradite the Hatfields indicted for the murder of the three McCoy brothers.

The killing continued. Once an old man of the Hatfield clan shot it out alone against the McCoy bunch, cursing his enemies with the last breath left in his bullet-ridden body. On New Year's Eve in 1888 a group of Hatfields surrounded Randall McCoy's cabin and set it afire in order to see the illuminated targets within. The same night a Hatfield shot a young McCoy girl to death and broke her mother's back.

Inevitably, the two clans began to find the warfare tedious, though there was also an economic factor which led to the diminished hostilities. About that time, commercial coal mining began to flourish in the area and as time progressed developers became less and less tolerant of the Hatfields' and McCoys' primitive behavior. They pressed the law to curb it, and offered a reward for the capture of Devil Anse Hatfield, which forced him into hiding. The developers then proceeded to buy up his land for a dollar an acre.

Old Devil Anse hid out in the hills near Omar until he died in 1921. For all his irascibility, he was apparently a man of humor and a superior naturalist, knowledgeable about the cultivation of ginseng, and the capture of bees as well as bears (once he tracked a bear through six counties and when he caught him there wasn't an ounce of fat left on the animal). He is now commemorated in Omar at the top of a steep, crooked path by a sizable statue, on the base of which are engraved the names of his loyal wife and thirteen children. The statue, fashioned in Carrara marble, was sculpted in Italy from photographs taken of the old man's corpse. It was imported by the Hatfield family at a cost of $3000, a sum no doubt collected from the many Hatfields who had by that time traded the violent and penurious career of feuding for the respectability of mine operators.

Down in the hollow, immediately below this burial ground, flows Main Island Creek, and there are those who believe that sometimes, when a cloud passes over the moon, you can see Devil Anse and his six penitent sons through the mist, descending the crumbling cemetery path into the waters of baptism.

ASA METERS

Altamount, North Carolina

Up in the Blue Ridge Mountains near the Tennessee border there's a legend which exemplifies how mountain folk, early despairing of civil authority, came to depend on the law of supernatural justice.

Asa Meters was a mean, ambitious, narrow-eyed man, not well liked by a people who instinctively distrust driving ambition. When Asa's brother was found dead, Asa claimed that his kin must have been careless and fallen on the pair of upturned sheep shears. Nobody believed him. Greedy Asa had impaled his poor brother, they thought, to get his share of the family farm. But there was no way to prove it, and the brother was buried in a shallow grave, without funeralizing, up in the field behind the house.

Years later, when Asa decided to plough up the field to sow what he hoped would be a profitable crop of rye, he hired a man named Holt to do the work. Along with everyone else, Holt still clung to the belief that Asa was a murderer. But he had learned a way to prove it.

If a victim's skull were placed over the head of a suspect, a confrontation and accusation would yield the truth. Holt ploughed the field with care and was able to disinter the dead brother's skull intact. It was twilight of the second day when he finished the job. A bad wind was coming up and already storm clouds furrowed the western sky. Soon cold, heavy rain began to fall and Holt, intending only to give the appearance of being eager for his pay, tramped into Asa's house, shaking moisture from his overalls and beating his hands against his upper arms to dispel the chill. While Meters huddled in privacy to count out the money owed, Holt planted the freshly-dug skull on the rafters above the slumbering hearth. Then he called, "Poke up your fire, Asa. Else it'll soon go out."

As Asa moved to the hearth and poked, his brother's skull grinned darkly overhead. Holt rose, removed the pipe from his mouth and pointed an accusing finger.

"Asa Meters, did you not slay your brother?"

Asa did not speak. But in the darkened, flame-flickered room he began to quake. He began to quake and he could not stop, not ever. From that moment forth the spirit of the murdered brother never left his side.

People say that Asa Meters could not eat because his brother snatched the food away; he could not sleep in his bed because his brother splintered the frame with an ax; and when at last Asa made himself a pallet of straw on the floor, his brother lay down, too, and nearly suffocated Asa by breathing in his mouth. Something gray, like a wavering cobweb, always hovered over the hearth, and in place of a horseshoe above the door, there appeared a pair of bloody shears. And when at last old Asa Meters died, a cat crept into the open pine casket and stole his soul away as a present to the Devil.

THE GHOST OF COLL WILLIAMS

Job, Kentucky

Crotchety Coll Williams was more than old enough to be Evylee's father but everybody in Job knew she'd married him for his property, a rich upland cornfield and a fine herd of cows. It surprised no one that when young Tom Gilbert crossed over from West Virginia, Evylee cast him a flirtatious eye.

Old Coll, who had suffered a bad attack of rheumatism during the winter, could do nothing but jealously fume and threaten. Two years later, still doubled up on what was now his deathbed, he shook his fist at his comely wife, vowing, "I'll git ye, Evy. I'll git ye." Evylee just laughed, buried him up in the cemetery knob under a cedar tree and calmly waited for the next passing preacher to give him a funeralizing and marry her to Tom.

But Evylee made a bad mistake. She failed to put up a gravehouse over Coll's mound to keep out "the varmint." In early days, mountaineers believed that unless some covering was erected over the burial place a small creature would burrow into the grave and disturb the departed's soul, which then would follow those responsible for the neglect. People were sure the varmint had gotten to Coll Williams, and when the funeralizing took place up on the hill it was with extra zeal that they sang Coll's favorite hymn:

> *Oh, brother will you meet me*
> *Meet me, meet me*
> *Oh, brother will you meet me*
> *On Canaan's far-off shore.*

At Evylee's wedding to Tom Gilbert the very next day, the singing and merriment took on a nervous edge.

Two days later, Deedy Craig, up on the hillside to lay phlox on her mother's grave, noticed a strange swelling on Coll's burial place. The mound had, in fact, almost doubled in size and it seemed to Deedy to be quivering slightly, almost as though it were breathing. Deedy scampered down in terror, and it wasn't an hour before the news reached Evylee that old Coll had been pestered by the varmint, and that he was romping around in his grave and raring to get out.

Evylee laughed 'til her sides ached.

The following afternoon Evylee ran in from the pasture calling to her new husband that the cows were down on their haunches in the chestnut grove and couldn't be budged. When Tom finally got one of the animals on her feet and into the sunlight, he tried to milk her to diagnose the complaint. Scarcely a cup entered the pail, and even that small amount didn't foam. When Tom dropped a silver coin into the bucket as a further test, the money turned black. Even before they smelled the cow's fetid breath both Tom and Evylee knew what the matter was. During the years he was laid up with rheumatism Coll had let the chestnut grove grow up. Grazing on the too-rich vegetation in that damp and shaded spot had made the cows "milk-sick," more than likely a terminal condition.

Evylee remembered Coll's threat and it made her mad as a hornet. She stomped up the knob through the chokecherry thickets to give the dead man a piece of her mind. The warm day was still; not a breath of air stirred. Yet when Evylee reached the summit the cedar over Coll's grave was swaying this way and that, and she could see the mound, now almost three feet high, heaving to and fro much like the cedar. She turned and ran.

Before the next dawn all but one of Evylee's cows were dead.

To keep the remaining cow in good health, Tom took an ax to clear the pasture of its lethal shade. While he was chopping, the ax bit cruelly into his shin. Even though Evylee smothered the wound in soot the bleeding wouldn't stop. She put him to bed and under the bed she put a double-edged ax, but still he bled.

She even took him up to the healer. The practitioner had once stopped the bleeding of a farmer who had sliced his heel string slap in two, and of a mule who'd fallen on a scythe, but he couldn't help Tom Gilbert. It was just too late and before the sun set, another hole was being dug just up the knob from Coll's grave.

The gravediggers couldn't help but notice the movement in Coll's towering mound. Great rollicking heaves turned first to spasms and finally gave only an occasional upward lunge—like someone exhausted by laughter. They never dug a grave quicker than they dug Tom Gilbert's.

After Tom was buried Coll's grave diminished until it looked like any other. Folks weren't convinced, however, that the old man had finished his devilment, because tendrils of poisonous moonseed soon clutched the new grave site, while the pinks and wild orchids that Evylee laid there turned limp and damp within minutes, as if pressed by an icy hand.

Evylee stopped visiting the cemetery and lived alone for all the rest of her days. No one ever heard her laugh again.

*Spectres of
the Waterways*

THE *RIVER BELLE*

Louisville, Kentucky
With the appearance of the steamboat came a grandeur and romance unprecedented in river life. When Nicholas Roosevelt's *New Orleans* first rounded the bend in the Ohio late one night in 1811, terrified Louisville citizens thought that either a comet had hit the river or that Tecumseh's Indians were inaugurating a raid.

Before a decade had elapsed, passage via steamboat was not only common, but was becoming the most elegant form of travel the country had ever known, as well as one fraught with danger and mystery.

For all the sumptuous ten-course meals, fine music, the thickest of carpets and enormous candlelit chandeliers, it was not impossible for disaster to strike when two arrogant captains decided to race their river queens. A mania for speed coupled with an overtaxed boiler could rip open a hull and cost hundreds of lives and a fortune in cargo. The clientele of the steamer was not always of the choicest sort. Always lurking near the respectable Mississippi belles and the affluent merchants were card sharks, well-dressed thieves, ladies of dubious morals and rascals of every kind. In the midst of such opulence and high passion the stage was inevitably set for nefarious behavior and, eventually, tragedy.

Supposedly among the handsomest of "floating palaces" to ply the Ohio in 1830 was one ill-fated craft named the *River Belle*. Like other elegant sternwheelers the *River Belle* offered passengers the very best of everything: steaming French coffee delivered to impeccably appointed staterooms in advance of the beefsteak breakfasts, never-ending rounds of planter's punch and mint julep, dancing until sunrise in a glittering ballroom and, of course, flawless and constant service. The *Belle* also offered a special ornament unlike any other vessel of its kind; the captain's beautiful wife. Captain Henry White was as fiercely proud of his ship as he was of his wife, who was a unique attraction for his passengers. Besides being lovely and sweet-tempered, the lady was an accomplished dancer and a much sought-after partner at evening parties. It should be firmly established that she was a constant wife, which no one doubted, for it was plain to all that though she enjoyed the admiration she attracted, she idolized her husband. Only a scoundrel would have attempted to take advantage of her—but eventually the scoundrel appeared.

At first the good-natured Captain White paid little heed to the attentions of the bounder, but as his wife seemed to grow more anxious, pale and wan, passengers on the *River Belle* noticed that White made sure that his wife retired early in the evening. Soon, she did not appear in the evening at all. Jealousy, it was whispered, had finally gotten the better of Henry White. Other strange occurrences were observed. Trays of food brought to the lady's cabin were left untouched outside the door. Her pet dog, a small friendly terrier, disappeared and at last the woman herself was seen no more. Two nights before the *River Belle* was due in Louisville, a gentleman taking a late stroll on the deck was passed by the scurrying form of a woman dressed in dark crinolines. As she hurried by, the man heard her speak. "A box, Henry. Please, I must have a box." The next evening the figure was seen by two more passengers. Each said they heard her crying for a box, and one claimed

that when she lifted her head only black holes were visible in place of eyes and mouth. Word of the ghastly vision spread to all corners of the vessel.

Captain White's dash and conviviality had long since left him; he appeared haggard and distraught. Passengers avoided him, and foreboding gripped them all. It was the competent pilot alone who guided the ill-fated *River Belle* into Louisville. The minute the steamer drew dockside there was a rush to disembark. For all those aboard the once gay craft, the journey had ended in nightmare, and no one would set foot on her planks again.

Still, there were those who pondered the fate of the captain's wife, and whether he had ruined his career simply to spite a flirtation. Several months later in the year 1831, one of the former passengers returned to Louisville. In the interim the city had been severely plagued by a cholera epidemic and the visitor was deeply affected by the empty, melancholy pall that shrouded its streets. Wandering along the foggy waterfront, he caught sight of the *River Belle*, sagging like a rickety wedding cake, with peeling paint and sadly damaged by vandals.

Seated on a nearby piling was a man the passenger recognized as the pilot of the *Belle*, to whom he directed a question about Captain White. In reply, he was told that the death of the Captain's wife had finished him on the river and that White had wandered south, nobody knew where. Ah, the visitor remarked, then the wife had died. "Oh yes, sir," replied the pilot. "Took with the cholera, you see. Captain had to bury her in the river before the *Belle* had reached Louisville. Couldn't let word get round the ship." He sighed and shook his head. "And not even a proper funeral nor a coffin. Fair broke his heart."

THEODESIA AND *THE PATRIOT*

Cape Hatteras, North Carolina

Some twenty-five miles off the coast of North Carolina lie the Diamond Shoals, bars of sand situated at the confluence of the Gulf Stream and the cold currents of the Arctic. Here, off Cape Hatteras, the two meet head-on, throwing up angry spumes of surf, sand and sea creatures in glittering confusion, as if the Devil himself were orchestrating some wild fandango to celebrate the downward spiral of tortured souls to the bottom of the sea. Here is the Graveyard of the Atlantic where countless ships and men lie subject to sea-floor sands which sift indifferently and ceaselessly through the skeletons of wood and bone alike.

This part of the Outer Banks is encrusted with legends. One of the most tantalizing unsolved mysteries is the enigma of *The Patriot*. This little packet ship is supposed to have set sail on December 30, 1812, bound for New York from Georgetown, South Carolina. Her single passenger was Theodosia Burr Allston, beautiful wife of South Carolina's Governor Joseph Allston and the daughter of Aaron Burr. Theodosia, who had recently suffered the loss of her only child, was presumably on her way to visit her father, once Vice President of the United States and notorious as the victor in a duel to the death with Alexander Hamilton. At the time of her departure, not only was Theodosia in ill health, but she was also burdened by the stigma of her father as a result of his conviction in 1807 for treason in the alleged plot to seize the government of Texas and Mexico.

The melancholy young woman never reached her destination. A storm struck Cape Hatteras when the *Patriot* was due to pass by, and the craft was never seen again. And oddly enough, no attempt to trace her was made by either Governor Allston or Aaron Burr. What investigations there were brought little to light, and it was not until 1833 that interest in the mystery was rekindled. An Alabama newspaper, *The*

Mobile Register, printed the sensational deathbed confession of a destitute old man who claimed to have been a pirate. He was, he said, a member of the crew who had captured and scuttled the *Patriot* and murdered all on board. Fifteen years later, in 1848, another self-confessed pirate claimed a part in the plot, adding that Theodosia Allston, choosing death over the favors of the captain, walked the plank with far more courage and dignity than any of her doomed cohorts.

Finally, in 1869, more tangible evidence of Theodosia's ill fate began to manifest itself. An ailing resident of the Outer Banks named Mrs. Mann was being attended by physician William G. Pool of Elizabeth City, North Carolina. Being too poor to pay the doctor for his services the old woman offered him the portrait of a beautiful woman which hung incongruously in her shabby bedroom. And she told the doctor a story about it. In 1812, she said, her sweetheart John Tillett and a group of cronies had come upon a small pilot boat with sails set and rudder lashed, drifting toward shore at Kitty Hawk. In an eerie silence, broken only by the creak of rigging and the slap of untended canvas, Tillet and his friends boarded the ship and found everything to be in order. There were no marks of violence and tidiness was paramount, extending even to a table set for food. Gingerly the group explored the ghostly ship, half expecting the heavy stillness to be rent by the moans of ghosts who once had walked these very decks in living form. Instead, they discovered a cabin like none they'd ever seen before. Elegant silk dresses spilled forth from a corner wardrobe. In another part of the room was a decorated brass-bound chest on which rested a handsome

bouquet of wax flowers and an intricately carved nautilus shell. And on the bulkhead hung the same striking portrait which now adorned the old woman's bedroom and which her beau had presented to her more than fifty years before.

Dr. Pool could see for himself how remarkable the painting was. Done in oil on a fine mahogany board and encased in a gilded frame, it portrayed a woman of perfect patrician beauty, with dark eyes and a snowy complexion tinged with a delicate rosy hue. Quickly smitten, Dr. Pool eagerly accepted it as payment for treating old Mrs. Mann.

For over a decade the portrait hung in the physician's house without his knowledge of its significance. One day Pool came upon an article describing the tragic history of the Burr family. Accompanying the text was an engraving of Burr's daughter. Immediately the startled doctor, recalling Mrs. Mann's story, realized the potential importance of his painting. He sent a photograph of it to a member of the Burr family and received a prompt reply: "We identify the portrait as a likeness of Theodosia Burr Allston who sailed to her death from Georgetown, South Carolina, on December 30, 1812." In rapid succession there followed other corroborations until it was established without doubt that the portrait in Dr. Pool's possession represented none other than Theodosia herself. But questions remain. Was the talented and forlorn beauty drowned in a storm off Hatteras, or was she forced to walk the plank by pirates? Why did neither her husband nor her father pursue an intensive search for her? And above all, why was she put upon such a frail schooner to negotiate the sinister shoals on her journey north?

KILL DEVIL HILLS

Outer Banks, North Carolina
Adjacent to Kitty Hawk, the scene of the first successful flight by the Wright brothers, this range of sandy hills fronting Albemarle Sound has half a dozen legends to account for its name. A sailor's theory holds that to navigate this treacherous part of the sound is enough to kill the devil. However, in 1728, William Byrd of Virginia, an ardent critic of North Carolina, presented another explanation: "Most of the Rum they get in this country comes from New England, and it is so bad and unwholesome that it is not improperly call'd Kill Devil."

Because a shore bird, the kildeer, frequents the region, a theory has been advanced that the hills became known as "Killdeer hills" and later Kill Devil Hills. It has also been noted that "Kill" was a colonial Dutch word for a small stream or channel and "devil" the name for a moving sand spout.

This is the land of the "Bankers." Of all Southern coastal people, the lives of early Bankers were the most firmly mullioned to the sea. Indeed, their ancestry began there, for it was the ocean's devastation of their ships which thrust the homeless seamen on these banks in the first place, and it was the sea that provided, along with nourishment, their livelihood. Before the turn of the century, hundreds of men from the area were directly occupied with the ferocity of the Outer Banks. Rescue crews, lighthouse tenders, salvage teams, lifesavers, wreck commissioners, even auctioneers who disposed of shipwrecked cargoes at shorefront "vendues," all played parts in the complex drama of combating and harvesting the sea. In such a unique and precarious society, unsavory rumors were bound to spring up and be supported by willing believers. To many shore people, the Bankers seemed to be plunderers, and there was a saying that a Banker would drop his mother's coffin in the street if he heard the cry of "Ship Ashore!" More vindictive is

78

the accusation that the Bankers were once land pirates who deliberately sought to wreck ships. On stormy nights greedy Bankers were supposed to have tied a lantern around the neck of an old horse and ridden the nag up and down the beach. Frightened sailors eager for the beckoning light of a sister ship were lured onto the hazardous reefs, hence the name of Nag's Head. When confronted with this story, a Banker smiles, lifts an eyebrow and asks if anybody has ever tried to secure a lighted lantern around the neck of a Banker pony.

One of the more colorful legends connected with the Kill Devil Hills tells of a ship wrecked off the Banks which yielded a hefty cargo. Guards were assigned to protect the barrels and boxes piled on the beach. During the first night the unwary watchmen dozed off, and awoke to find several items missing. The second night the guard was doubled, and before their unbelieving eyes they saw a large bale detach itself from the others and float off into the night. Terrified, the men fled, convinced that what they had witnessed was the work of the Devil. However, the following night an old Banker called Evil Ike volunteered for the job of watchman. As soon as he saw one of the cartons begin to slide away into the darkness, Ike, armed with a gun and a lantern, plunged after it. The illumination soon solved the mystery. Mike Rush was up to his old tricks. Using a line tied to his beach pony, Mike was dragging the booty off across the sand. Quickly Evil Ike cut the rope, fired his gun into the air and looked on gleefully as Rush and his frightened pony raced away down the beach. In the morning Ike was able to report to his colleagues that there would be no more trouble, for he had killed the Devil.

Still another tale is told of a Banker who made a bargain with the Devil to exchange his soul for a bag of gold. A midnight meeting was arranged on top of the tallest dune, but as the appointed hour approached, a fierce, howling wind arose. Shouting through the roaring gale, the Banker commanded the Devil to throw down the bag of gold and advance to claim his half of the deal. The Devil hurled down the gold and leaped forward—straight into a deep pit dug by the Banker to trap his adversary. Within minutes the fiend was covered by racing drifts of sand. The Banker had gained a fortune, and the Devil had been killed.

BLACKBEARD AT BATH

Bath, North Carolina

Of all the pirates who plagued the Atlantic Coast, Edward Teach was unquestionably the most fearsome. Huge, arrogant, brawling, effluviant of blood, sweat and alcohol, this outrageous character raised in the swill-filled gutters of Bristol, England, was known to the honest seamen of Colonial America as "a swaggering merciless brute." His appearance was awesome. Pistols and daggers corseted him; the enormous greasy beard covering his face clear to the eyes was plaited into little pigtails and tied with colored ribbons. Before a battle it was his wont to insert under his hat pieces of hempcord which he set afire, letting them burn like punk to illuminate the devilish glare of his bulging eyes and the snarl on his raw, curling lip. Before this Mephistophelian spectacle, many a merchantman, who otherwise might have fought manfully, found his courage quickly withered, and deferred to Blackbeard with hardly a struggle. Even his own crew were terrified of him, but they remained loyal partly because he was so open-handed and relatively generous with the booty collected, and partly because they foresaw the awful consequences if they incurred his displeasure. They did, in fact, see the consequences almost every day. When a victim refused to part with a jeweled ring, Captain Teach sliced the ring-bearing finger off with his cutlass. When a tavern keeper tarried on his trips to and from the rum barrel, he would find himself the target for gunplay.

If ever this seafaring ogre could be said to have had a home port on the continent it was Bath, North Carolina. Bath was beautifully suited to his needs; it was within comfortable sailing distance of the shipping lanes from Europe, thus giving access to good pillaging, and it offered convenient hideaways in the inlets and around the sandy islands of Pamlico Sound, one of which, Ocracoke, became Blackbeard's favorite refuge for careening his ships. Bath merchants were eager to purchase pirate plunder and most important, the officials were friendly. Northern ports had begun cracking down on sea thieves, but in 1718 the government of North Carolina readily honored King James' offer to pardon all pirates upon their agreement to abandon this troublesome career.

In January Edward Teach sailed two ships into Bath and surrendered to the Governor under the terms of the Act of Grace. The Governor at that time was Charles Eden, who maintained his capital in a splendid mansion on the Pamlico River. It is said that he and Blackbeard understood one another at a glance. Neither had the slightest intention of honoring the mother country's frangible treaty, and reputedly the two struck up a dicey partnership. Teach set up his headquarters, the foundations of which still remain today, at Plum Point across Bath Creek from Eden's home. From this structure, the pirate proceeded to build a tunnel, which also still exists, running from a hole in the steep, myrtle-tangled bank under the creek to the Governor's stone wine cellar. In exchange for a share in the plunder Eden provided storage space. At one juncture Eden's secretary, Tobias Knight, was tried and acquitted for improper dealings with Teach, but Eden himself was never implicated.

Among the plentiful Blackbeard legends none is stranger than the one which declares that Governor Eden's partnership included granting the pirate the right to court his beautiful daughter, Elizabeth. Now, Teach's relations with women were unusual. Women were the one chink in his armor for, despite his cruelty to men, he could melt with infatuation over every barmaid, trollop or harbor girl who caught his fancy. In his constant state of inebriation while ashore, Blackbeard was almost certain to marry somebody before his departure. By the time he met Elizabeth he already had thirteen wives though, apparently, no woman mystified or intrigued him more than the elegant and aloof Elizabeth Eden. Aloof she surely was, for her heart belonged to another fairer and nobler seaman. Blackbeard was nonetheless persistent. In a desperate effort to elude his uncouth, blubbery attentions Elizabeth bribed two of her father's slaves to help her escape. In the dead of night the two men rowed her down Bath Creek to a point where she could disembark and make her way to the old Marsh house, taking refuge there with her friend, Margaret Palmer.

Enraged by the lady's disappearance, the titanic Teach set out on an orgy of destruction southward, capturing as his first prize Miss Eden's lover, whom he mutilated and threw into the sea. He then returned to Bath.

Several weeks passed. Since Blackbeard had made no further overtures, Elizabeth felt it safe to leave Miss Palmer's haven and return home. As she and the chambermaid were packing her valise a servant knocked at her bedroom door and entered bearing an oblong box

wrapped in scarlet silk and fastened with laurel blossoms. The footman did not know who had delivered the package nor was there any card attached.

Gently the mystified Elizabeth removed the flowers and drew off the wrap to reveal an exquisite polished teak box inlaid with mother-of-pearl. Its beauty took her breath away, while its contents, when she lifted the lid, inspired a scream of horror. She crumpled unconscious to the floor as she dropped the box, out of which rolled its grisly treasure; her lover's severed hand.

Shortly after the above drama supposedly occurred, it is recorded that objections began to mount from North Carolina landowners over Governor Eden's laxity with Blackbeard's exploits and his crew's molestations of resident wives and daughters. Governor Spotswood of Virginia felt obliged to exert pressure to remedy the situation. In November of 1718, Spotswood sent forth an expedition commanded by the pirate-hating Captain Robert Maynard who, after a dramatic battle with Teach at Ocracoke Inlet, sailed back to Bath with the pirate's gargantuan, blood-matted head swinging from the end of the bowsprit.

And Miss Eden? Legend claims she languished, slowly pined away and died of a broken heart. History tells us otherwise; there was no such person for Charles and Penelope Eden were childless. Margaret Palmer was not born until 1721 and the Marsh house was not built until 1744 at the earliest.

Was so brutal a tale made from whole cloth or, despite the inaccuracies, is there some shred of truth to it all? That such an evil deed *could* have been done is sure enough. Perhaps it is prudent that we know no more than that.

Men at Work

JOE BALDWIN'S LANTERN

Maco, North Carolina

One soft, steamy evening in the spring of 1889, a train bearing President Grover Cleveland paused near the Maco Station fifteen miles west of Wilmington, North Carolina, to take on wood and water for the rest of the journey to Washington. The President, stepping down for a brief stroll along the tracks, was mystified to see a signalman down the line carrying two lanterns—one red and one green. When he questioned the conductor about the necessity for colored lanterns, the trainman replied, "Mr. President, it's like this: if the signalman didn't carry two lights and if they weren't colored, engineers on down the way couldn't tell it wasn't Joe Baldwin's lantern looking for his head, or his head looking for his lantern, depending on how you figure it."

The legend of Joe Baldwin's light began more than twenty years earlier on a wet night in 1867. Along about midnight on that date, Conductor Baldwin, riding in the rear coach of a Wilmington, Manchester and Augusta train, felt the car slowing down. In an instant he realized what had happened. The car had come uncoupled from the rest of the train and was simply coasting without power of its own. In the next instant, Baldwin looked back down the track behind the loose car and saw, gleaming a quarter of a mile behind, the beam of a following locomotive. Seizing his lantern, Joe raced to the rear platform of his coasting car and frantically waved his light to warn off the pursuing train. But the engine's fiery eye bore down on the stranded coach, and in the splintering crash that followed, Baldwin was decapitated and both his head and his lantern were propelled high through the night into a nearby swamp.

After the accident, a weird light began to appear on the swamp side of the Maco track, seeming always to weave to and fro about five feet from the rails. In 1873 a second light appeared, and the two would pass back and forth by each other like illuminated cable cars. One light, they'd say, was carried by Joe searching for his head, and the other was carried by the head searching for Joe. In the glare of the lanterns neither recognized the other. Later when the two lights diminished to one, folks were still sure it was Joe Baldwin carrying his lantern, endlessly searching.

The phenomenal performance continued. A U.S. Army detachment from Fort Bragg was stationed briefly at Maco and made attempts to

perforate the mystery. They couldn't. A scientist from Washington, D.C. was sent to Maco to establish his theory that the light was simply a will-o-the-wisp, a delusion and a figment of local superstition. He failed. Joe reported promptly every night during the scientist's stay.

At his whim he is still reporting. Some say moist, moonless nights are the best times to see Joe's ghostly light. Others say neither the weather nor the season make any difference at all. His spectral lantern will swing only when he chooses to swing it, as it has now for more than a hundred years.

SWIFT'S SILVER

Paint Creek, Kentucky

"It's near a peculiar rock, boys. Don't never quit hunting for it. It will make Kentucky rich."

These dying words of advice from blind old John Swift in 1800 have inspired treasure hunters ever since. Even today, every once in a while, someone—a farm boy perhaps—will feel his hoe strike metal in a hillside cornfield and believe that he has discovered the legendary treasure hidden by Sailor John more than two hundred years ago.

In the middle of the eighteenth century when some settlers shot a big Wolfe County bear, the mortally wounded creature fled into its den, and when the hunters followed they found a rich vein of silver inside. Before the white men could exploit the wealth, Shawnee Indians slaughtered everyone in the group except a lad named George Munday, whom they adopted and pressed into helping them mine the precious metal. According to legend, Munday drifted from the Shawnees to the Cherokees, then to Spanish miners and finally to French woodsmen. At the beginning of the French and Indian War, Munday fought on the side of the French, and although they defeated General Braddock's troops in July of 1755, Munday was taken prisoner by the British and eventually found himself in Alexandria, Virginia. Alone and starving in a strange town, Munday was befriended by the English sailor, John Swift. In exchange for Swift's kindness Munday told him of the huge Kentucky silver lode. In the succeeding eight years, after returning to the site, Swift, Munday and two others mined and smelted a fortune in silver bullion. Unable to transport all of the treasure out of the state, the men left most of it buried in Kentucky.

Back once more in Alexandria, Swift again felt the call of the sea. He set sail for England but only after planning to return in three years for another trip to Kentucky with his companions. But once in England

the sailor's loud criticism of the King and his Colonial exploiters fetched him quickly to prison. After fifteen years in a darkened cell, John Swift, now blind and ailing, was released to return once again to Kentucky in a last pitiful search for his buried wealth. Munday and one of the other adventurers had since been killed leaving Swift with but one remaining friend. For fourteen more years he hobbled sightlessly up and down the rocky cliffs on the arm of this single guide, seeking the Kentucky El Dorado until at last he died, his spirit broken and his body wasted.

But John Swift had been a disciplined man, and during his first foray into the mining business he had kept a journal and had drawn maps of the middle Kentucky River country which, through the years, have mysteriously duplicated themselves and fallen into the hands of many treasure seekers. None of these speculators have had any luck, and in time the description of Swift's 'peculiar rock' has changed. Some say the rock is turtle shaped with marks like turkey tracks running across it; some say it nestles close to a bank where three white oaks grow from a common stump. But there are still others who say that John Swift never did sail back to England. Some maintain that the crafty sailor, armed with maps, accompanied by Munday, two Indians and two Frenchmen, returned instead to Kentucky from Alexandria.

When Swift once again saw the vast treasure spread out before him, his mad greed triumphed. As all the others slept, he thrust his flashing blade into their hearts. Rich beyond belief, but alone and without porters to bear his fortune back to civilization, Swift returned empty-handed to Virginia where the wild old man with his tales of silver was at once thought to be crazy. The more desperate he became, the more shrilly he raved and the less he was trusted. Before anyone could be found who would consent to help Swift retrieve the treasure, his eyesight failed, thus insuring that the old man would never see his fortune again.

No one else has seen it since, either.

TWO MINING TALES

It used to be that unless a man's corpse could be accounted for after a coal mine disaster, his widow would receive no compensation. In Logan County, West Virginia, there is a tale of this practice which has a satisfactory ending. In the early 1920's after a severe explosion which had closed off Section Five on the main run of the Q—Mine, all the miners, dead or alive, had been accounted for except one Frank Cooper, the father of six children. Frank's time card hadn't been punched either in or out, and the mine owners felt no obligation to compensate his wife, suggesting instead that Frank had deserted her.

A miner named Louie was assigned to set new beams in the damaged area and clean the section so new track could be laid. Louie was enormously strong and fearless and always the first to plunge in to help with the most dangerous repair work. In this instance, since not one of his co-workers was willing to assist him, Louie agreed to go it alone. As he went deeper into the mine the air became thinner. Water dripped from the walls of the shaft. Now and then, in the dusky passageway, he heard a rat scurry by. But there was another sound, as well. Turning around, Louie saw that he was being followed by a second miner.

"Well now," said Louie. "Glad to see one of you ain't afraid."

The other didn't answer, and as he came closer, Louie saw that the man's skin had a milky blue pallor to it and his eyes were so sunken into his head that they were not visible at all. Nevertheless, this gaunt figure seemed to possess as much strength and drive as Louie. After the two men had erected the first beam and Louie had commenced scraping away the loose debris for the second, his gaunt helper abruptly snatched the shovel from Louie's hand and spoke harshly. "No. Not there. Over here." Obediently the puzzled Louie began to prepare the designated ground for the second post. He hadn't dug out more than a foot of slag when he came upon the remains of a human hand. When

Louie whirled around to report the discovery to his helper the man had vanished. For the first time in his life Louie felt the hackles of fear rising on his neck. At once, he announced the finding of a body to the authorities.

At home on the following night, Louie was awakened by a knocking at his door. Outside in the darkness stood his strange companion from the mine. His voice was faint, but his bluish gums seemed bent into a smile. "Thank you," he sighed. "Now I can rest, and my family will be cared for." Before Louie's eyes the figure began to fade until only the black of night crowded round the door.

In the morning Louie learned that miner's tags had identified the corpse as that of Frank Cooper.

One of the dreaded hazards of coal mining used to be the blasting of sulphur balls. These meteor-like formations can range from the size of a basketball to a lump weighing several tons. Because they are so hard, they are almost impossible to drill and have had to be removed with explosives. When a miner heard the cry "Fire in the hole!" he hastened for any cover he could find. Frequently accidents occurred. A heavy blast near weak ribbing could bring down the roof, burying any miner unlucky enough to be below. In the 1920's this is what happened in Grant Town—except that the tragedy wasn't entirely accidental.

Young Fox Carter and Aaron Conoway were both sweet on pretty Terry Hite, though there didn't seem to be much reason for a contest. It struck folks that handsome, strapping Carter was a far better catch than shy, runty Aaron, whose only mark of distinction was a remarkable pair of boots—pointed, fancy-stitched and laced in blue. Boots, however, don't service a romance. Nevertheless, people couldn't help noticing that Terry seemed to be favoring Aaron. And neither could Fox Carter.

On the day of the disaster in the South Main Section there were four men working: Carter, Conoway, Leo Pasinski and Leo's thirteen-year-old son. The boy had moved away from the others for a drink of water at the time of the cave-in and it was only by chance that he saw the slate and coal come crashing down on his father and Conoway. This was not all that he saw, but the terrified boy was unable to report, until years later, that the hulking Fox Carter had clearly shoved Aaron Conoway into that deafening black downpour.

Both bodies were recovered, although one of Aaron's legs had been sliced off by the falling debris and was missing. They never even found the boot. Both funerals were held on the hillside, and every week Fox Carter was seen to lay a spray of primroses or bouncing bet on Aaron Conoway's grave.

After a while Terry Hite agreed to marry Fox and the whole town

turned out for the festivities. The two made a good-looking couple, though Fox looked rather pale during the ceremony and kept glancing distractedly down at his side, away from his bride. Soon the men in the mines began to notice further peculiar behavior on Fox's part. South Main, where the accident had occurred, had long since been repaired but Carter resisted going near it. Once when it had been necessary to pass through the section to avoid another cave-in, he had seemed petrified, his eyes popping, and had bolted like a frightened horse. Another time, when the buggyman was opening the mantrip doors for a load of miners, Fox cried out, "Shut the doors. Don't let it in."

His wife noticed his strange ways, too. Every evening he arrived home panting and would hurriedly bar the door behind him. He gobbled his gritbread and greens as though the food would be snatched away, all the while glancing suspiciously around the room. At night he twisted and turned under the flock tick and, most curious of all, took to sleeping with his boots on.

Terry tried every remedy she knew. She gave him tea of boneset leaves for insomnia and tonics of sulphur and molasses laced with cherry-bark moonshine. As her grandmother had taught her to do, she surreptitiously cut a lock of hair from her husband's head and pegged it in the hole of a sycamore tree to ward off fits. But the day a blackbird flew out of the paw-paw bushes and into the cabin, Terry knew that death was coming to fetch her man.

They brought home his body at nightfall, just as the last light was fading behind the tree-spiked mountain ridge. It wasn't a cave-in, they told her, nor an explosion. There hadn't been any sort of disaster. Fox and another miner had been assigned to work South Main. No sooner had the men entered the section than Fox had rushed out screaming and fallen straight across the tracks of an oncoming buggy. His wild, final utterance, cut short by death, was, "It's coming! It's com-"

In the wet slag just behind his body, the miners found the imprint of a single pointed boot.

Women

FRANKIE SILVERS, MURDERESS

Kona, Yancy County, North Carolina

Early on a brisk December morning in 1831 Frankie Silvers dropped in on her mother-in-law, announcing smugly, "I've done all my day's washing and scrubbed the woodwork, too." She added, however, that she was worried about her husband who hadn't returned from purchasing his Christmas whiskey. "Gone all night and not a sign of him yet," she said.

Search parties went to every river crossing, but no one found hide nor hair of Charlie Silvers. Soon, however, everyone accepted the fact that Charlie had probably drowned, even though there was no proof.

A neighbor, old Jake Collis, was less satisfied with the investigation. His careful exploration of the missing man's cabin in the Blue Ridge hamlet of Kona revealed numerous fresh ax-blade scars at the base of the hearth, and the briskly scrubbed floor boards still showed traces of what could be blood stains. Subsequently, human teeth and hacked up bones were found in the hearth ashes. When warmer weather came, two hounds, sniffing and digging under a laurel bush, brought to light what looked like the remains of a human heart.

The hand of the law clamped down on Frankie Silvers. She was taken to Morganton, tried, convicted and sentenced to death.

Family loyalty dies hard in mountain country, and Frankie's kin managed to sneak her out of jail in a wagon loaded with hay. But the suspicious sheriff followed the cargo. When he ordered his men to search through the load, Frankie, dressed as a man, sprang out and asked in a deep voice if the sheriff wanted to buy some hay. "No thank you, Frankie," replied the sheriff. "We don't want no hay. We want you."

Back in the Morganton jail, Frankie, realizing her plight was hopeless, made a full confession. Yes, she had murdered her husband; there had been another woman. Yes, she had hacked him to pieces and burned

101

his remains; and yes, indeed, she had reported the truth to her mother-in-law on that frosty morning—that she had done her day's washing and scrubbing; in fact she had scoured all night too, to rid the cabin of any sign of her crime of jealousy.

And the heart, she was asked. Why did she cut out the heart and bury it? Frankie's face closed up like a burr. After a while she lifted her chin and said in a steady voice, "Because it were mine."

During the trial many people felt that Frankie hadn't told all she knew about the murder. Some thought that perhaps her kinfolk had assisted her on that bitter night. When she ascended the scaffold in July of 1833 and seemed about to speak, her father shouted from the crowd, "Die with it in you, Frankie." But all Frankie wished to do was to recite the fourteen-stanza poem she had written in prison. After she had spoken her piece, she ate a slice of cake, pulled the black hood over her head and was hanged by the neck until she was dead.

In those days the corpse of a criminal was often turned over to

medical students for dissecting. Female bodies were especially hard to come by, which Frankie's father knew. His daughter's remains, he was heard to say, were not to be knifed up by anyone. Very probably he felt about her heart the way she had felt about Charlie's: it belonged to him. To prevent Frankie's corpse from being discovered he had dug seven graves, all of which were filled in by dawn following the execution. Frankie's body was first hidden in a tavern near Morganton and then buried in a private cemetery, beneath a spread of Christmas ferns.

Frankie Silvers was the first woman to be hanged in North Carolina, and even today the words of her mournful poem, set to an eerie tune, are sung on lonesome nights in the back country:

> *Farewell, good people, you all now see*
> *What my bad conduct brought on me;*
> *To die of shame and disgrace*
> *Before this world of human race.*

BELLE BOYD, SPY

Front Royal, Virginia

Some women seem to flourish on intrigue and dark duplicity; unquestionably Belle Boyd was one of them. Although Mathew Brady's merciless camera revealed "The Siren of the Shenandoah" to be less than beauteous, Belle was certainly one of the most fascinating, adroit, and daring young women of her day. In 1862 an army correspondent for the *Philadelphia Inquirer* presented this description of her: "There was a kind of Di Vernon dash about her, a smart pertness, a quickness of retort and utter abandonment of manners and bearing which were attractive from the very romantic unwontedness." Even Northern newspapers acclaimed her as the most remarkable figure since Joan of Arc.

This flower of Southern womanhood, said to be equally at ease in the ballroom and on the battlefield, was only seventeen when the War between the States began, at which time she, of course, immediately committed her passions to the Confederate cause. On the second day of occupation of her hometown of Martinsburg, Virginia, Federal troops entered the Boyd home to check out a report that a Confederate flag was concealed therein. It was evening when these uninvited guests arrived, and Belle was upstairs dressing to receive a favored suitor. When she heard the stomping of boots on the veranda below her bedroom and looked out to see a Northern sentry attending the Union officers' horses under the magnolias she became enraged. Nevertheless, she completed her toilette and with a dazzling smile, which she felt confident would conceal her fury, descended to the drawing room to greet the unexpected and unwelcome visitors. The commanding officer was so overcome with her flirtation, he allowed himself to be lured into an adjoining room where Belle drew a revolver from the folds of her demure pink skirts, shot him dead, and had a couple of livery boys bury him beneath a dogwood. Thus began her notorious career which attained its zenith at Front Royal in 1862.

Belle and her mother, attempting to reach Richmond, had been denied passes and thus were detained at Front Royal's Strikler House, a hotel familiar to Belle—so familiar, in fact, that she knew that she could spy on the first-floor parlor where Union officers held war councils from a closet with a hole in the floor in the room above. (Just how Belle had made the discovery is a matter for speculation.) Anyway, one evening after supper as she was passing the parlor, she heard the din of voices from within. Hastening up to the second-story room she entered the darkened closet and closed the door behind her. Through the hole in the floor she saw General Nathaniel Banks and a group of officers bending over a map table in the smoke-filled room below. She smelled their tobacco, and she heard their plans.

Belle's strategy was immediately conceived and cleverly contrived. Within the hour General Banks and all his staff were invited to a ball on the 22nd of May. Belle, of course, was to host it. Within the next

hour Belle was on a fast horse riding through a driving rain to the headquarters of Stonewall Jackson. And minutes before the first gray wash of dawn, Belle, wet through, had returned and was creeping stealthily up to her chambers at Strikler House.

The May ball was a resounding success. Music, refreshments and favors were combined to perfection. Wreaths of pink roses encircled the chandeliers and a scattering of petals adorned the punch bowl. Each officer was presented with a small quill pen fashioned from the feather of a blue jay, the tip encased in silver. Belle won all hearts, especially that of General Banks, whom at one point in the festivities she playfully draped in a Confederate flag and then waltzed him up and down the room.

It was a weary and sublimely sated group that straggled back to headquarters in the early morning, and it was an ebullient Stonewall Jackson who, half an hour later, captured 750 of the one thousand Union troops at Front Royal.

JENNY WILEY, PIONEER

East Point, Kentucky

One of Kentucky's many indomitable pioneer women was a courageous young soul named Jenny Wiley. In 1787 a settler named Matthias Harmon founded the first fort in the valley of the Big Sandy River. Veined by the river and its tributary creeks and locked on three sides by the dark green hills and indigo mountains, this was dangerous territory, the last part of Kentucky to be surrendered to the white man by the Indians.

Living at Harmon's Station with her five children and fifteen-year-old brother was Jenny Wiley. In the autumn of 1787 when the majority of the men were on a hunting trip, a group of Shawnee and Cherokee raiders descended on Jenny's cabin at Walkers Creek. Because of the ferocity of the attack Jenny judged that the Indians had mistaken her home for that of Matthias Harmon who had defeated them several days before. But she was unable to reason with the angry, blood-thirsty band or even to fight back. Before her eyes the Indians tomahawked her brother and four of her children. They then burned the cabin to the ground and left the settlement, taking Jenny and her fifteen-month-old baby as prisoners. During the year that Jenny was held captive she was treated to the spectacle of seeing her "leastun's" brains dashed out against a butternut tree.

The following winter when the tribe had left Cherokee Creek on

one of their hunting trips, Jenny, bound by cowhide thongs, crawled to a corner of the shelter in which she was imprisoned and she crouched beneath a leak in the roof until rainwater had loosened the leather bands. Then this singular woman, weakened by semi-starvation and inactivity, escaped down Little Mud Lick Creek, up another small creek (later

named for her), and finally crossed the river at East Point on a cotton-wood log, reaching the safety of Harmon's Station only seconds before the pursuing Indians.

Her strength and fortitude is forever memorialized at her grave in the town of River, Kentucky, northeast of Paintsville.

Places

PRIEST'S FIELD CHAPEL

Middleway, West Virginia

Adam Livingston of Middleway, West Virginia, was not only obstinate, but a man of little faith as well. In the year 1790, a traveler whom Livingston had taken into his comfortable house among the rolling fields and orchards of this northeastern corner of the state fell violently ill. As the visitor's condition worsened, he begged his host to send for a priest. Livingston refused, saying there was no priest nearby, and even if there were he would not allow one in his house. When the stranger died Livingston's servants prevailed upon him to hold a wake. Grudgingly Livingston agreed to this, for he valued his servants' good opinion, and candles were lit and brought to the room of the dead man. But no sooner had they been carried through the door than they were extinguished by a sudden rush of damp wind. Hurriedly and without ceremony, Livingston buried the corpse.

And his troubles began.

His barn burned, his money vanished. When locked chests and closets were opened, out tumbled clothes either in shreds or riddled with tiny holes. Neighbors who came to call inevitably departed with their garments marred by star-shaped rents. Worst of all was the constant snipping sound of shears heard throughout the house both night and day, to Livingston far more torturous and sinister than the nightly thunder of phantom horses galloping around the yard.

In vain, Livingston appealed to a minister and to his friends. No one could help him. One night in a dream there appeared to Livingston a man in flowing robes. Certain that the apparition was a priest, he set off in haste to Shepherdsville to fetch Father Dennis Cahill. The priest returned with him to Middleway, said Mass in the house and immediately the manifestations ceased.

Overcome with relief and gratitude, Livingston at once bequeathed

to the Roman Catholic Church thirty-four acres of his property on the banks of the Opequon Creek, specifying that a chapel should be built on the land.

Time passed but the Church made no move to erect a chapel. Livingston eventually sold the remainder of his land and went to spend the rest of his life in Pennsylvania. Many years after his death, his heirs made claim to the broad field he had left to the Church. It was not until then that the Church, in order to abide by the terms of the bequest and thus hold the land, put up a small gable-roofed building known as Priest's Field Chapel. The year was 1925, more than a century and a quarter after the weird occurrences in Adam Livingston's house.

Once a year, in September, a Mass is conducted in the Church.

THE REELFOOT LEGEND

Reelfoot Lake, Tennessee

Before December 16, 1811, this western Tennessee area was a region of thick forest threaded through with little streams. The series of earthquakes which continued from December until March 15, 1812, transformed the terrain. Landslides rumbled down the steep bluffs of the Mississippi, banks caved in, whole islands vanished, and twenty-inch-thick cottonwood trees snapped like twigs and were swirled away by the wild waters. After the tumult had passed what emerged was a glorious lake.

The Chickasaw tribe, to whom the land belonged, knew the reason for the phenomenon—a tragedy as fraught with sorrow and bravery as the ancient tales handed down by their forefathers, a story that gave the lake its name.

On the bluffs across the Mississippi from the old Spanish settlement of New Madrid, Missouri, there lived a band of Chickasaws whose chief was afflicted with a club foot. Kalopin, or Reelfoot as he was called, was shunned by all the maidens of the band, for a firm prerequisite in an Indian brave was fleetness. In a final desperate attempt to find a wife Reelfoot gathered together several friends and crossed over to Choctaw territory. While he was smoking a peace pipe with the chief, Copish, he was startled by the sight of a merry-faced Indian maiden, swift and delicate as a fawn. Immediately he pointed the girl out to Copish, declaring that she was the woman he must have for his wife. Infuriated, the Choctaw chief rose and dashed the peace pipe to the ground. The charming creature that the lumbering Chickasaw had singled out was Laughing Eyes, the only daughter of Copish.

Reelfoot implored; he offered fine gifts of beaver skins and lustrous mussel pearls. Copish turned a deaf ear and Reelfoot, forlorn, returned home. He thought of Laughing Eyes constantly; he considered stealing her. Although he was warned in a dream of the terrible things that would happen to an Indian guilty of wife-stealing—that the waters would cover his village and drown all his people—Reelfoot was determined to have the girl.

Early in December, after the corn had been gathered in, Reelfoot, accompanied by some of his braves, fell upon the Choctaw settlement and carried off Laughing Eyes to be his bride. No sooner had the

wedding day dawned than the earth began to rumble and tremble. Darkness descended, thunder boomed, and the Father of Waters roared into Reelfoot's village. A few Indians ran deep into the forest to escape disaster, and the last thing they saw was the giant parting of the earth into which swarmed the furious waters, carrying Reelfoot, his bride and many of his people, who lie today at the bottom of the lake.

THREE
CREEKS

Hyden, Kentucky
Monroe, Tennessee

Two creeks in the forested area of Hyden, Kentucky, received their names via the frustrations of one early pioneer. While driving his oxen through one of the swollen streams the man and his beasts received so many painful abrasions from the sharp rocks that he immediately labeled the offending body of water Cut-Shin. The following day he experienced an even more rugged creek-traverse and was moved to exclaim, "Well, by jeeminy, this is Hell-fer-Sartain." In fact, the whole terrain is so stoney that legend insists that the Devil, skipping from hilltop to hilltop bent on burdening the countryside with boulders, accidentally let fall his whole load. Even today any severe outcropping of rocks is met with the remark: "The Devil must have broken his apron strings hereabouts."

Farther to the southwest in Monroe, Tennessee, near Dale Hollow Reservoir, flows another storied creek. Once upon a time two Cherokee braves wooing the same girl asked their chief to judge which of them should have her. Wishing to be just, the chief suggested that both young men toss twigs into the nearby creek and that the piece which floated furthest downstream would indicate who should have the maiden.

The first Indian chose the very lightest curl of birch bark. The second pricked his fingers twisting off the spikey upper stalk of a horse nettle. The drops of blood on his fingers amused his rival. But when the time came to toss the bits into the water the coil of birch bark was whorled rapidly to the bottom of the brook, while the nettle head, airy as a tumbleweed, bobbed along the water's surface until it disappeared around a bend. Since that day this particular stream has borne the name Nettle Carrier Creek, gratefully bestowed by the victorious suitor.

The Dead

Compared to the simple, stern and sometimes cabbage-patchy older graveyards of New England, the bedecked burial grounds of the Border States are like intricate gardens, frequently and unashamedly revealing the whims of those interred.

In the Maplewood Cemetery on the outskirts of Mayfield, Kentucky, is buried a successful horse trader and breeder named Henry Wooldridge, whose eccentricity led him to hire stone masons to sculpt life-size statues not only of the bachelor himself mounted on his favorite horse "Fop," but of all his family. The fifteen statues, completed during Wooldridge's lifetime at a cost of $6,000, all face east and surround his vault. Included in the group are a fox, a deer, two dogs and a likeness of Henry's only love, Susan Neely, who was killed in an equestrian accident in her youth. It is said that her devoted suitor wore their engagement ring until he died in 1899 at the age of seventy-seven.

Along a stream at the mouth of the Elk River in West Virginia, a man found it necessary to carve his own epitaph. In 1795 William Strange, a member of a surveying party, wandered away from his camp and was never found alive. Years afterward, forty miles from the spot where he was last seen, two travelers passing along the bank of Turkey Run Creek came upon a pile of bones beneath a giant beech tree. Leaning against the trunk was a rusted musket with the shot pouch still dangling from the ramrod. Carved in the bark was this verse:

> *Strange is my name and I'm on strange ground*
> *And strange it is I can't be found.*

Immediately the stream was renamed, and is known to this day as Strange Creek.

Stewartsville Cemetery in Scotland County, North Carolina, is an old burying ground where many of the monuments are decorated, not to anyone's surprise, with thistles. The Reverend Colin Lindsay's grave is not in the least peculiar except if we consider that another grave came close to preventing his existence at all. Back in Scotland a young woman who was later to become Lindsay's mother was interred in the family vault before she was actually dead. Thanks to some grave robbers seeking her jewels, the lady fled the dreadful tomb, recovered her health, and several years later gave birth to Colin, who came to America in 1792.

Until 1939, visitors could actually view the remains of Mrs. Charles B. Hansel in the Oakdale Cemetery in Henderson, North Carolina. Mrs. Hansel suffered from tuberculosis and before she died she requested that she be buried where the sun would always shine upon her. Numerous lenses were placed on the top of her tomb so that her skeleton was not only warmed by the sun but visible to passersby. Although the coffin is now covered it is still known as the Tomb of the Sunshine Lady.

However, at Resthaven Cemetery in Harlan County, Kentucky, a glass-covered coffin is still visible which contains the remains of a woman who for all her life was afraid of the dark. She requested that her burying box have a glass window and that a light be kept burning at night. Her husband saw to it that her wish was granted, and added this inscription: "Meet me in heaven, 'Mom'."

Not far away, up in Wallens Creek, an old couple became so doubled up with rheumatism that when death fetched them they had to be buried in their rocking chairs.

In the old burying ground of Jamestown, Virginia, there stood a huge sycamore for more than a century. Its stump still separates the tombs of Reverend James Blair and his wife Sarah. Sarah's father, Colonel Benjamin Harrison, was violently opposed to the couple's union and swore an oath to separate them. His curse was, at any rate, effective after death.

But it is in the Custis Cemetery on Virginia's eastern shore that spite and bitterness reached a zenith. The graveyard, fifteen miles south of Eastville, is near the site of the original Arlington estate for which George Washington's adopted grandson, George Washington Parke Custis, named the more celebrated Arlington house and cemetery. And it was his grandfather, John Custis IV, who was buried here in 1749.

About fifty years prior to that event, Custis, then the gallant of the colony, married Frances Parke, its leading belle. To expect these two spoiled and self-willed young people to form an ideal couple would have been folly and, of course, they did not. Relations between them began to deteriorate right away, and within a short time they had ceased

125

communication and addressed each other only through a slave named Pompey.

"Pompey, ask your master if he will have coffee or tea, sugar or cream."

"Pompey," Colonel Custis would reply, "Tell your mistress I will have coffee as usual, with no cream."

One day Colonel John unexpectedly invited his wife for a drive, and for some unknown reason Frances accepted. The Colonel set off, directing his horse and carriage toward the Chesapeake Bay and then straight into it. When the water began to creep over the floorboards Frances asked, "Where are you going, Colonel Custis?"

"To Hell, madam," replied the Colonel.

"Drive on," said Frances. "Any place is better than Arlington."

At that remark Custis turned his carriage around toward home, saying, "Madam, I believe you would as lief meet the Devil himself if I should drive to Hell." Whereupon his wife replied, "Quite true, Sir. I know you so well I would not be afraid to go anywhere you go."

This sparring match apparently cleared the air enough to enable the couple to reach a property settlement. Soon afterwards Frances died of smallpox. When John's time came in 1749, he left all his property to his son with the proviso that an English marble stone be set over his grave bearing "an inscription at once so unchivalrous and so vindictive as to give it place among the annals of Virginia as a crime against good manners and good taste." The last four lines make perfectly succinct the Colonel's sentiments:

Aged 71 years & Yet liv'd but Seven Years which
was the space of time He kept a Batchelers
house at Arlington on the Eastern Shore
of Virginia

BIBLIOGRAPHY

Arnow, Harriette Simpson. *Flowering of the Cumberland*. New York: Macmillan Co., 1963.
———. *Seed Time in the Cumberland*. New York: Macmillan Co., 1960.
Banta, R.E. *The Ohio*. New York: Rinehart, 1949.
Border States, The. New York: Time-Life Books, 1968.
Botkin, B. A. *Treasury of Mississippi Folklore*. New York: Crown, 1955.
———. *Treasury of Railroad Folklore*. New York: Crown, 1953.
———. *Treasury of Southern Folklore*. New York: Crown, 1949.
Callahan, North. *Smoky Mountain Country*. New York: Duell, Sloane & Pearce, 1952.
Clark, Thomas D. *The Kentucky*. New York: Farrar, Rinehart, 1942.
Comstock, Jim. *The Best of Hillbilly*. New York: Pocket Books, 1968.
Federal Works Project Series. *Kentucky*. New York: Hastings House, 1954.
———. *North Carolina*. Chapel Hill: University of North Carolina Press, 1955.
———. *Tennessee*. New York: Hastings House, 1949.
———. *Virginia*. New York: Oxford University Press, 1941.
———. *West Virginia*. New York: Oxford University Press, 1941.
Kephart, Horace. *Our Southern Highlanders*. Outing Publishing Co., 1913.
Leighton, Clare. *Southern Harvest*. New York: Macmillan Co., 1942.
LIFE Treasury of American Folklore. New York: Time, Inc., 1961.
McMeekin, Clark. *Louisville, the Gateway City*. New York: Julian Nessner, 1946.
———. *Old Kentucky Country*. New York: Duell, Sloane & Pearce, 1957.
Moore, Charles. *The Family Life of George Washington*. New York: Houghton Mifflin, 1926.
Musick, Ruth Ann. *The Telltale Lilac Bush*. University of Kentucky, 1965.
Peattie, Roderick, ed. *The Great Smokies and the Blue Ridge*. New York: Vanguard Press, 1943.
Rankin, Hugh F. *The Golden Age of Piracy*. Virginia: Colonial Williamsburg, 1969.
Stick, David. *Graveyard of the Atlantic*. Chapel Hill: University of North Carolina, 1952.
———. *The Outer Banks of North Carolina, 1584-1958*. Chapel Hill: University of North Carolina, 1958.
West Virginia Hillbilly, wkly ed. Richwood, West Virginia.
Whipple, A.B.C. *Pirates: Rascals of the Spanish Main*. New York: Doubleday, 1957.
Wigginton, Eliot, ed. *The Foxfire Book*. New York: Doubleday, 1972.